THE POETRY OF ALUMINUM

The Poetry of Aluminum

Walter the Educator™

SKB

Silent King Books a WhichHead Imprint

"Earning a degree in chemistry changed my life!"
– Walter the Educator

dedicated to all the chemistry lovers, like myself, across the world

CONTENTS

WHY I CREATED THIS BOOK?

Creating a poetry book about the chemical element of Aluminum was an interesting and unique endeavor for several reasons. Firstly, poetry has the power to transform seemingly mundane or overlooked subjects into something meaningful and captivating. By exploring the properties, history, and significance of Aluminum through poetry, I can shed light on its often-underestimated value and beauty. Additionally, poetry allows for creative expression and experimentation, enabling for the exploration of the various aspects of Aluminum in a lyrical and imaginative way, which can engage readers in a new and unexpected manner, making them appreciate the element's significance in our lives and the world around us.

ONE

WE SHALL ADORE

In the realm of elements, a shining star,
Aluminum, you are, both near and far.
With atomic number thirteen, you stand proud,
A metal so versatile, we sing aloud.

From humble beginnings, in Earth's crust you dwell,
A treasure untapped, a secret to tell.
Bauxite, your ore, buried deep in the ground,
We mine and refine, a treasure we've found.

Oh Aluminum, your lustrous sheen,
Reflecting the light, a vision serene.
Strong and lightweight, you soar through the skies,
In planes and spaceships, you truly rise.

A conductor of electricity, you connect,
Wires and cables, through which currents project.
In kitchens and homes, your foil we employ,
Preserving our food, a simple joy.

Aluminum, in construction you play a role,
From towering skyscrapers to bridges that span whole.
A foundation so sturdy, a support so strong,
In buildings and structures, you belong.

Oh Aluminum, you're malleable and ductile,
Forged into shapes, both beautiful and tactile.
From cans to cars, you take many forms,
A testament to your versatility norms.

But let's not forget, your humble origins,
In soda cans and kitchen utensils, your dominions.
Recyclable and sustainable, you make our world bright,
Reducing waste, a beacon of light.

Aluminum, you've revolutionized our lives,
With ingenuity and innovation, you thrive.
In laboratories and industries, you shine,
A testament to human intellect divine.

So let us applaud, this element so grand,
Aluminum, in our world, you firmly stand.
From the Earth's crust to the products we adore,
Aluminum, forever we shall adore.

TWO

OH, ALUMINUM

In the realm of shimmering light,
A metal strong, yet ever so light.
Aluminum, the element divine,
A marvel of nature's design.

Silvery sheen, like the moon at night,
Aluminum gleams, a radiant sight.
Born from bauxite, in Earth's embrace,
Forged by fire with ethereal grace.

Versatile, it bends to the will,
Crafting wonders with skillful thrill.
From towering skyscrapers, reaching high,
To humble cans that hold our supply.

A conductor, it conducts the flow,
Of electricity, where currents go.
In wires and cables, it carries the spark,
Connecting us all, even in the dark.

Oh, Aluminum, you're truly grand,
A symbol of progress across the land.
Recyclable, you're born anew,
Sustainable, your cycle true.

From planes that soar in the azure sky,
To cans that hold our favorite pie,
You touch our lives, both near and far,
A symbol of human ingenuity, a shining star.

So, let us marvel at you, Aluminum,
For you've shaped our world, every crumb.
Innovation owes you its due,
Oh, Aluminum, we admire you.

THREE

CREATIVE HAND

In a realm of gleaming wonders,
Where versatility knows no bounds,
There resides a metal so pure,
A marvel that forever astounds.
Aluminum, the shining star,
A symbol of human ingenuity,
With strength and lightness combined,
It shapes our world with true serenity.
From towering skyscrapers,
To humble kitchen utensils,
Aluminum's grace is unmatched,
Its adaptability, truly surreal.
In the fiery depths of smelters,
Where bauxite yields its treasure,
Aluminum emerges, molten and free,
Ready to fulfill its destined measure.

It dances with the winds,
In the wings of mighty planes,
Aiding our dreams to take flight,
With resilience that never wanes.

From the depths of the ocean,
To the vastness of outer space,
Aluminum's reach knows no bounds,
A testament to its enduring grace.

Oh, Aluminum, a gift divine,
In every industry, you excel,
A silent hero, the unsung star,
Innovator of the material spell.

So let us raise a toast,
To Aluminum's brilliance so grand,
A testament to human progress,
A symbol of our creative hand.

FOUR

CONDUCTIVITY

Aluminum, the metal of grace,
With shimmering beauty, it fills the space.
A versatile friend, so strong and light,
In every industry, it shines so bright.

From aerospace to construction tall,
Aluminum stands proud, never to fall.
In planes and rockets, it takes to the sky,
A testament to its strength, oh so high.

In buildings and bridges, it lends its might,
Supporting structures, day and night.
Its malleable nature, a gift so grand,
Molded and shaped by skilled hands.

In cans and foils, it wraps our food,
Preserving freshness, ensuring it's good.
Its conductivity, a boon to behold,
Powering circuits, a story untold.

From cars to bicycles, it glides with ease,
Efficient and nimble, a gentle breeze.
In the kitchen, it cooks with flair,
Durable and non-toxic, beyond compare.
Aluminum, a metal of endless worth,
Transforming industries, reshaping the Earth.
A testament to human innovation and skill,
With Aluminum, the possibilities fulfill.

FIVE

VERSATILE WAYS

Aluminum, a metal so fine,
Shining bright, oh, how you shine.
Versatile element, so many uses,
In industries, you never lose.
From airplanes soaring high in the sky,
To cans that hold our favorite pie.
In buildings tall, you lend your might,
Structures strong, reaching great heights.
In electrical wires, you conduct with ease,
Powering our world, bringing us peace.
In cooking pots and pans you're found,
Heating our meals, spreading joy all around.
Aluminum, oh, how you amaze,
With your strength and versatile ways.
From spacecraft to bicycles, you're ever in demand,
A metal so precious, crafted by hand.

You're lightweight yet sturdy, a paradox indeed,
A material that fulfills our every need.
In packaging and foils, you protect and secure,
Preserving freshness, ensuring things endure.

Aluminum, you're a metal of might,
A symbol of progress, shining so bright.
From cars to electronics, you play your part,
Bringing innovation, igniting a spark.

So here's to Aluminum, a metal so grand,
With infinite possibilities, you expand.
Innovative and adaptable, you lead the way,
A true marvel of chemistry, we proudly say.

SIX

THICK AND THIN

Aluminum, a versatile alloy,
A metal of strength and endless joy.
With silvery sheen, and light as air,
In countless industries, you're always there.

From airplanes soaring through the skies,
To cars that speed, their engines rise.
In buildings tall, you stand so firm,
A testament to your strength, we affirm.

In cans and foils, you wrap our food,
Preserving freshness, it's understood.
In electrical wires, you conduct with might,
Powering our homes, day and night.

Your presence felt in every space,
From kitchen utensils to outer space.
With creativity, we mold your form,
Making wonders, in every norm.

Aluminum, you shine so bright,
A metal that brings us sheer delight.
Innovation's companion, through thick and thin,
Forever cherished, our beloved Aluminum.

SEVEN

TRULY DIVINE

In the realm of elements, a shining star,
Aluminum, versatile, both near and far.
With strength and lightness, it takes its place,
A metal of wonder, full of grace.
From airplanes soaring high above,
To cans that hold the food we love,
Aluminum, your impact is vast,
In industries where you're unsurpassed.
In construction, you form the frame,
With durability that bears no shame.
Skyscrapers reach for the skies,
Built upon your strength and rise.
In cars and bikes, you play a role,
Reducing weight, enhancing control.
Efficiency is your greatest claim,
As you help us move, swift and tame.

Recyclable friend, you're eco-friendly,
Sustainable, preserving Earth's beauty.
For you can be used again and again,
Reducing waste, a noble gain.

Oh Aluminum, you're a gift to behold,
Innovative, adaptable, worth more than gold.
In every facet of life, you shine,
A metal of the future, truly divine.

EIGHT

GREAT LENGTH

In the realm of conductivity,
A shining light, a luminosity,
Aluminum, you grace the stage,
In every industry, you engage.
From wires that carry electric might,
To cookware that withstands the heat's bite,
You conduct the energy, you transmit the flow,
In circuits and cables, you effortlessly glow.
But beyond your conductivity, dear friend,
Your versatility knows no end.
You're molded and shaped with skillful hands,
Creating wonders across the lands.
In aerospace, you reach new heights,
With your strength, you take daring flights.
From planes that soar through the open sky,
To rockets that explore realms up high.

In cars and vehicles, you find your place,
Reducing weight and increasing pace.
With your lightness, you enhance the speed,
Making journeys seamless, fulfilling every need.

From packaging materials to buildings tall,
You're the backbone, standing strong and tall.
In windows and doors, you provide strength,
In construction and architecture, you go to great length.

Oh, Aluminum, you're truly grand,
Innovation and progress, you command.
Your presence in our world, so vast,
A metal that forever will last.

NINE

STRENGTH AND INGENUITY

Aluminum, a mighty metal, strong and true,
With versatility that knows no bounds,
In countless industries, it shines anew,
A staple of progress, where it resounds.

In buildings tall, it stands with steadfast pride,
A foundation, sturdy, yet light as air,
Its strength supports, its durability beside,
With aluminum, architects dare.

In planes and cars, it soars through the sky,
Reducing weight, increasing speed,
A metal ally, never asking why,
Innovation fueled by its very creed.

In wires and cables, it conducts the flow,
Electrical currents, they dance and play,

Efficiency, reliability, it bestows,
Connecting the world, day by day.
In packaging and foils, it finds its place,
Preserving freshness, protecting goods,
A barrier against time's relentless chase,
Ensuring quality, as it should.
Aluminum, you weave your magic spell,
In every industry, you leave your mark,
A metal that empowers and excels,
Creating wonders, even in the dark.
So let us celebrate this element great,
A symbol of strength and ingenuity,
Aluminum, we bow to your weight,
Forever a part of our shared history.

TEN

IMMENSE WORTH

In factories and labs, a metal shines bright,
With versatility that's a wondrous sight.
Aluminum, the element we adore,
A substance we can't help but explore.

In planes, it soars through the sky,
Light and strong, it helps them fly.
From cars to bikes, it's a crucial part,
With its strength and durability, it's truly smart.

In packaging, it keeps things secure,
Preserving goods, we can be sure.
From cans to foils, it's a trusted shield,
Ensuring freshness, it never yields.

In construction, it builds structures tall,
With its adaptability, it stands proud and tall.
From windows to doors, it's a sturdy frame,
Resisting the tests of time and flame.

In electronics, it conducts with ease,
Powering our gadgets, it's a true tease.
From laptops to phones, it's an essential wire,
Connecting us all, igniting our fire.

In space, it ventures to the unknown,
Crafting rockets, it's a stepping stone.
Exploring the universe, it takes its place,
Guiding our dreams, with grace and grace.

Aluminum, a metal of immense worth,
In every industry, it proves its birth.
With each new discovery, we're in awe,
Forever grateful for this metal's flaw.

ELEVEN

INNOVATION'S FIRE

In industries vast, Aluminum is found,
A metal abundant, both strong and renowned.
From airplanes soaring high up in the sky,
To cans that hold drinks, as time passes by.

Its adaptability, a remarkable trait,
In structures it's used, both early and late.
From buildings towering with beauty and grace,
To bridges connecting, with strength and embrace.

In transportation, it plays a vital role,
From cars on the road to ships on the shoal.
Its strength and durability withstand the test,
As wheels keep turning, on journeys abreast.

But Aluminum's magic goes beyond these domains,
In electrical applications, it truly reigns.
Conductivity, a gift it possesses,
Powering circuits with endless successes.

In packaging, it shines, a material of worth,
Preserving our food, protecting the earth.
From cans to foils, it wraps with precision,
Keeping freshness intact, a remarkable mission.

And in the realm of architecture, it thrives,
As buildings take shape, where dreams come alive.
Its versatility, unmatched and profound,
Creating structures, both modern and renowned.

In electronics, it sparks innovation's fire,
As circuits come alive, taking us higher.
From smartphones we hold to screens that we view,
Aluminum's touch enhances the view.

And even in space, its presence is known,
From rockets to satellites, it has grown.
Exploring the cosmos, expanding our reach,
Aluminum's use, a lesson it does teach.

So let us celebrate this metal so grand,
Aluminum, a marvel, in every land.
From industry to industry, it does transcend,
With its adaptability, strength, and trend.

TWELVE

FOREVER IN OUR NAME

In industries, you'll find me strong,
A versatile metal, I belong.
Aluminum, my name, I shine bright,
With properties that bring delight.

In aerospace, I soar up high,
Aiding flights that touch the sky.
From planes to rockets, I take flight,
With strength and lightness, day and night.

In cars, I lend my sturdy frame,
Reducing weight, improving the game.
Efficiency and speed, I enhance,
Aiding vehicles in every chance.

Recycling is where I truly shine,
Sustainable, a friend of thine.

I'm endlessly reborn, again and again,
Preserving resources, for a greener domain.
Aluminum, in so many ways,
I serve mankind, throughout the days.
From construction to transportation,
Sustainability, my dedication.
So, raise a toast to Aluminum's might,
A metal that shapes our world so bright.
With strength and versatility, I proclaim,
Aluminum, forever in our name.

THIRTEEN

ELEMENT'S ALLURE

In a realm of elements, stands Aluminum proud,
A metal so versatile, its virtues allowed.
From aerospace soaring, to structures so grand,
Aluminum's touch transforms every land.

Its strength, unmatched, a sturdy embrace,
In buildings it shelters, defying time and space.
From bridges suspended, to towers that gleam,
Aluminum weaves dreams, a visionary's theme.

In planes and rockets, it takes to the skies,
A lightweight companion, with grace it flies.
Transportation's ally, from cars to the seas,
Aluminum whispers progress, with every gentle breeze.

In electronics, it hums, conducting the flow,
A conductor of currents, where data does grow.
From wires to circuits, it sparks innovation,
Aluminum's adaptability, a true revelation.

But beyond these realms, its magic extends,
To packaging and cans, a cycle that mends.
Recyclable hero, a sustainable choice,
Aluminum's echo, a harmonious voice.

In nature's abundance, it's found all around,
A gift to mankind, both sturdy and sound.
Its brilliance shines bright, like the sun's golden ray,
Aluminum's legacy, forever to stay.

So let us applaud, this element's allure,
For shaping a world, that is brighter and pure.
Aluminum's essence, in every creation,
A testament to progress, a symbol of elation.

In industries vast, its mark will remain,
A testament to strength, that nothing can wane.
Aluminum, we celebrate your might,
A metal of wonder, forever in flight.

FOURTEEN

STRENGTH AND GRACE

Aluminum, a marvel of strength and light,
A metal that gleams with silvery might.
In aerospace, you soar through the sky,
With wings made of aluminum, you fly so high.

In construction, you stand tall and strong,
Supporting the structures that last long.
From towering skyscrapers to bridges wide,
Aluminum, you're the backbone with pride.

In electronics, you conduct with grace,
Carrying currents at a rapid pace.
From smartphones to laptops, you play your part,
Aluminum, you're the conductor of the art.

In transportation, you speed on the road,
With aluminum bodies, a sleek and bold ode.

From cars to bikes, you're lightweight and fast,
Aluminum, you're the future that's built to last.
Oh, Aluminum, you're versatile and true,
A metal that shapes the world anew.
In every industry, you find your place,
A testament to your strength and grace.

FIFTEEN

REALM OF LIGHT

Aluminum, oh noble metal so bright,
With strength and versatility, you ignite.
From Earth's crust, you emerge, shining so bold,
A treasure of nature, worth more than gold.

In industries vast, your uses extend,
A metal of wonders, a true godsend.
In buildings and planes, you find your place,
Aiding in progress, with elegance and grace.

In architecture, you shape the skyline high,
As towering structures reach for the sky.
Sleek and modern, your presence is clear,
Reflecting the future, with no trace of fear.

In electronics, you flow like a current,
Conducting signals, so swift and fervent.
From smartphones to laptops, you power the way,
Connecting the world, with every display.

In space exploration, you venture afar,
Aiding the dreamers, who dream of the stars.
With spacecraft and satellites, you take flight,
Unveiling the mysteries of the cosmic night.

Aluminum, your role in the world is profound,
A metal of wonders, forever renowned.
With strength and adaptability, you shine bright,
Guiding us forward, in the realm of light.

SIXTEEN

METAL SO GRAND

In the realms of industry, Aluminum shines,
A metal versatile, strength it defines.
From towering structures to electronics grand,
It shapes our world, with a sturdy hand.

In architecture, it stands tall and true,
Supporting buildings, reaching for the blue.
Its lightness and strength, a perfect blend,
With Aluminum, grand designs ascend.

In the realm of transportation, it plays a part,
From cars to airplanes, it makes them smart.
Reducing weight, improving efficiency,
Aluminum propels us with great efficacy.

Recycling its essence, sustainability's key,
For Aluminum can be used again, you see.
From cans to vehicles, it gets a new lease,
A metal so precious, never to cease.

In nature's embrace, Aluminum resides,
In rocks and minerals, where it hides.
A gift from the Earth, a treasure to find,
Aluminum's presence, a marvel to bind.

Conducting electricity, it does with grace,
Connecting circuits, powering our space.
In electronics, its prowess is renowned,
Aluminum, a conductor, forever renowned.

As the future unfolds, Aluminum's might,
Will shape our world, with a dazzling light.
In space exploration, it reaches for the stars,
Aluminum, the metal that takes us far.

So let us celebrate, this metal so grand,
Aluminum, a marvel, in every land.
With strength and versatility, it leads the way,
Forever shining, in the light of day.

SEVENTEEN

ECO-FRIENDLY CHOICE

In the realm of architecture, strong and true,
There lies a metal, shining like new.
Aluminum, oh marvel of the Earth,
A substance of value, of infinite worth.
    In buildings tall, with grace and might,
You lend your strength, a shining light.
Skyscrapers rise, reaching for the sky,
Aluminum beams hold them up high.
    In electronics, you play a vital role,
Conducting currents, connecting the whole.
From wires to circuits, you bring them to life,
Aluminum, conductor of power and strife.
    In space exploration, you've left your mark,
Aiding rockets as they embark.

Light yet sturdy, you venture afar,
Aluminum, a companion, guiding each star.
    And in sustainability, you stand tall,
Recycled and reused, you never fall.
An eco-friendly choice, a symbol of hope,
Aluminum, a friend, helping us cope.
    So let us sing praises to Aluminum's name,
For its contributions, its everlasting fame.
In architecture, electronics, space, and more,
Aluminum, a marvel we truly adore.

EIGHTEEN

WONDROUS ELEMENT

In beams of strength, Aluminum takes its place,
A metal mighty, with elegance and grace.
In construction's realm, it stands tall and true,
Supporting structures, holding skies of blue.
From towering skyscrapers to humble abodes,
Aluminum weaves dreams and molds.
With its lightness and durability combined,
Architects and builders forever find,
A material that's strong, yet light as air,
Creating wonders that seem beyond compare.
In transportation's realm, it plays its part,
From cars to planes, it's a work of art.
Reducing weight, increasing speed,
Aluminum propels us, fulfilling our need.
With wings that soar and engines that roar,
It carries us to destinations we adore.

But there's more to Aluminum, for it's green,
A champion of sustainability, unseen.
Recyclable and abundant, it paves the way,
For a future where waste has no say.
From cans to gadgets, it finds new life,
In a world where sustainability is rife.
So let us celebrate this wondrous element,
That shapes our world with fervent intent.
In construction, transportation, and sustainability,
Aluminum shines with versatility.
A metal that's strong, yet light and green,
In our endeavors, it remains unseen.

NINETEEN

ALUMINUM'S MIGHT

In structures tall, Aluminum stands strong,
A pillar of support, where it belongs.
With grace and poise, it holds its weight,
A metal so versatile, it's hard to debate.
Conducting electricity with ease,
Aluminum wires weave through industries.
From power lines to cables, it plays its part,
Connecting the world, from end to start.
In airplanes soaring through the skies,
Aluminum wings help them to rise.
Light and sturdy, it defies gravity's pull,
A marvel of engineering, both bold and cool.
In packaging and cans, it keeps things fresh,
Preserving flavors, a true success.
Recyclable and sustainable, it leads the way,
Reducing waste, day by day.

So raise a toast to Aluminum's might,
A metal with endless uses, shining so bright.
From buildings to gadgets, it's always there,
A vital element, beyond compare.

TWENTY

CONSCIOUS EARTH

In the realm of electrons, it dances with grace,
Aluminum, the conductor in this cosmic space.
From starlit skies to our earthly domain,
It weaves its magic, a conductor's refrain.

In circuits and wires, it conducts with might,
Electrons flowing freely, a symphony of light.
From power lines to the devices we hold,
Aluminum's role, a story yet untold.

In space exploration, it takes flight,
Crafting vessels to explore the night.
From rockets to satellites, it lends its hand,
Aluminum, the traveler, to distant lands.

But it's not just in space where it finds its worth,
Aluminum's presence is felt here on Earth.
In buildings and structures, it stands tall,
A testament to its strength, one and all.

From bridges to skyscrapers, it shapes our world,
With Aluminum's touch, our dreams unfurled.
And in the realm of technology, it's no surprise,
Aluminum's role, a beacon that never dies.

In electronics and gadgets, it finds a place,
Enabling our connections, a digital embrace.
From smartphones to laptops, it powers our days,
Aluminum, the conductor, lighting our ways.

And let us not forget its sustainable might,
Recyclable and abundant, shining so bright.
As we strive for a greener, more conscious earth,
Aluminum's legacy, a testament of its worth.

So let us celebrate this wondrous element,
Aluminum, the conductor, ever-present.
From space to architecture, technology, and more,
Aluminum's versatility, forever we adore.

TWENTY-ONE

ARCHITECTURE TO ART

In the realm of elements, shining bright,
A metal that embraces both strength and light,
Aluminum, a marvel, with wonders untold,
Its story unfolds, a tale to be told.

In the realm of electronics, it takes the lead,
Conducting electricity with remarkable speed,
From smartphones to laptops, it plays its part,
Connecting the world, with a spark in every heart.

In the realm of space, it ventures high,
A companion to satellites, reaching the sky,
Light and resilient, it conquers the unknown,
Exploring the cosmos, to realms yet unshown.

In the realm of sustainability, it stands tall,
Recyclable and eco-friendly, answering the call,

From cans to cars, it reduces our plight,
Preserving our planet, shining bright.
In the realm of design, it leaves its trace,
Its malleability and beauty, a work of grace,
From architecture to art, it inspires anew,
Unleashing creativity, in all that we do.
In the realm of progress, its fame shall endure,
A symbol of innovation, forever secure,
Aluminum, the element, oh so grand,
We celebrate your contributions, hand in hand.

TWENTY-TWO

SUSTAINABLE HERO

Aluminum, conductor of might,
Invisible currents, it holds so tight.
Through its veins, electricity flows,
Connecting the world, wherever it goes.
From space exploration to skies so vast,
Aluminum rockets, soaring so fast.
Its strength and lightness, a perfect blend,
To reach the stars, where dreams transcend.
Sustainable hero, it stands tall,
Recycled and reused, never to fall.
Infinite cycles, it gracefully weaves,
Preserving our Earth, as nature perceives.
Aluminum, oh metal divine,
A treasure so rare, we're blessed to find.
In every atom, its secrets unfold,
A marvel of science, forever untold.

TWENTY-THREE

INFINITE WORTH

In the realm of conductivity, you shine,
Aluminum, a metal so divine.
With electrons dancing through your core,
You conduct electricity, forevermore.

In power lines, you carry the charge,
A conductor strong, both large and small.
From homes to factories, you light the way,
With every surge, you proudly display.

In airplanes soaring through the sky,
You lend your strength, never asking why.
From wings to fuselage, you support the flight,
Aluminum, you bring dreams to new height.

In cans and foil, you find your place,
Preserving freshness with your embrace.
From kitchens to picnics, you're always there,
Keeping our food safe and ready to share.

In construction, you shape the land,
From skyscrapers tall to bridges grand.
With durability and strength so true,
Aluminum, we owe so much to you.

In sustainability, you lead the way,
Recycled and reused, day after day.
A metal so versatile, a gift to the earth,
Aluminum, your worth is of infinite worth.

So let us celebrate your shining grace,
Aluminum, you're a marvel to embrace.
From industry to homes, you light our days,
With your brilliance, our world forever stays.

TWENTY-FOUR

ENDLESSLY GRAND

In a world of conductivity, it shines,
Aluminum, the metal, so divine.
With electrons dancing, it conducts the flow,
Bringing light and power wherever we go.
A conductor of energy, strong and pure,
Aluminum, the element we adore.
From power lines above to wires below,
It carries the current, making life glow.

In buildings and homes, it forms a shield,
Protecting us from lightning and its yield.
Its strength and lightness, a perfect blend,
A sustainable choice, from start to end.

In planes and cars, it soars through the air,
Reducing weight, increasing speed with flair.
Its versatility, a gift to behold,
In every industry, its story is told.

Aluminum, oh aluminum, how you inspire,
With your properties that never tire.
A metal so vital, so endlessly grand,
In our world, you will forever stand.

TWENTY-FIVE

PROGRESS
AND MIGHT

In a world of technology so grand,
Where progress and innovation expand,
Aluminum, the element so bright,
Shines with a captivating light.
From smartphones to laptops, it plays a role,
A conductor of signals, a vital soul,
With its lightweight and sturdy frame,
It brings our digital dreams to acclaim.
In space exploration, it takes its flight,
Crafting vessels that pierce the night,
To the moon and beyond, it carries our dreams,
Unveiling the mysteries of celestial streams.
Sustainable and recyclable, it stands tall,
Reducing our impact, protecting us all,

For in aluminum's embrace we find,
A material that's gentle and kind.
   So let us celebrate this element so fine,
Its contributions to our modern design,
Aluminum, a symbol of progress and might,
Guiding us towards a future so bright.

TWENTY-SIX

UNION SO RARE

In the realm of technology, Aluminum shines,
A metal of versatility, it defines.
With strength and lightness, it takes its place,
In the heart of progress, a vital embrace.
From sleek devices to towering towers,
Aluminum's touch empowers.
Designers marvel at its malleable grace,
Crafting wonders, leaving a lasting trace.
Sustainability, its noble call,
Recyclable, it stands tall.
Resisting corrosion, it weathers the storm,
An eco-friendly choice, a sustainable norm.
Aluminum, the metal of the future,
Innovation's ally, a constant nurturer.
Advancing industries, igniting sparks,
A beacon of hope in the world's arc.

So let us celebrate this element divine,
Aluminum, our ally in design.
Bound to the future, forever we'll share,
A bond of progress, a union so rare.

TWENTY-SEVEN

CELESTIAL EMBRACE

In a realm of atoms, I emerge, refined and true,
Aluminum, the conductor, my purpose I pursue.
With electrons dancing, I conduct the flow,
Connecting worlds with energy, a vibrant glow.

From towering structures to bridges grand,
I lend my strength, unwavering, to the land.
Versatile and resilient, I stand tall and strong,
In car engines and planes, I belong.

In kitchens and pantries, where freshness resides,
I guard the flavors, preserving them inside.
A shield against time, I keep nature intact,
In cans and foils, a guardian, that's a fact.

Industries embrace me, for I'm a wonder to behold,
From aerospace to technology, my worth unfolds.
In satellites and spacecraft, I voyage through space,
Unveiling the mysteries of the celestial embrace.

So, let me shine, oh world, in all my brilliance bright,
Aluminum, the element, a beacon of light.
A conductor, a protector, a creator of new,
In every endeavor, I'll always be there for you.

TWENTY-EIGHT

ENDLESS DELIGHT

Aluminum, the guardian of freshness,
Preserving flavors, sealing tightness,
In foil wraps and cans it resides,
Keeping food safe, a trusted guide.
A metal of strength, yet light as air,
In construction, it's beyond compare,
From towering skyscrapers to airplanes high,
Aluminum's might reaches the sky.
Sustainable it stands, a beacon of green,
Recyclable, renewable, a shining sheen,
Its life cycle endless, no waste in sight,
Aluminum, a champion of the fight.
Versatile companion, in every field,
From transportation to the power it wields,
In cars and bikes, ships and trains,
Aluminum's touch, innovation reigns.

In packaging, electronics, and more,
Aluminum's role we can't ignore,
From kitchen to space, it finds its place,
A metal of wonder, full of grace.
Oh, Aluminum, you shine so bright,
A metal that brings us endless delight,
Forever we'll cherish your presence true,
Aluminum, we owe so much to you.

TWENTY-NINE

LOW DENSITY AND DURABILITY

In industries, you shine, Aluminum, so bright,
A metal that brings progress with its light.
From construction to transportation, you play your part,
A versatile element, a work of art.

In planes and cars, you soar through the sky,
Your strength and lightness, none can deny.
In buildings tall, you stand strong and true,
Supporting structures, a testament to you.

In packaging, you keep our food secure,
Preserving freshness, ensuring it endures.
From cans to foil, you're a shield so strong,
Keeping our sustenance safe all day long.

In space exploration, you reach for the stars,
With satellites and rockets, you travel far.

Your low density and durability,
Make you the metal of choice with great ability.
Aluminum, you're sustainable too,
Recyclable and abundant, it's true.
With endless possibilities, you inspire,
A metal that never fails to inspire.
So here's to Aluminum, a wonder to behold,
A metal that shines with a story untold.
Innovative, versatile, and strong,
You shape our world, where progress belongs.

THIRTY

SHIELDING POWER

In the realms of technology, Aluminum shines,
A metal so versatile, it never confines.
Its strength and lightness, a perfect blend,
A marvel of science, from end to end.
From space exploration to the skies above,
Aluminum's prowess, it's sure to prove.
Satellites and shuttles, soaring high,
In Aluminum's embrace, they touch the sky.
Sustainability's champion, Aluminum's role,
Recyclable, eco-friendly, a treasure to behold.
From cans to cars, its purpose so vast,
Reducing our carbon footprint, a future so vast.
Packaging protector, Aluminum's might,
Preserving our goods, day and night.
Its shielding power, a fortress so strong,
Ensuring freshness, nothing goes wrong.

In every industry, Aluminum does reside,
Inspiring progress, with each stride.
A conductor of electricity, a beacon of light,
Innovation's ally, shining so bright.
So let us celebrate this element divine,
Aluminum, a metal that continues to shine.
From technology to sustainability's quest,
Its legacy and impact, forever blessed.

THIRTY-ONE

SHIMMERING SURFACE

Aluminum, a shimmering light,
A metal with a radiant might.
Born from Earth's abundant crust,
In industries, you earn our trust.
From planes soaring in the sky,
To cars that swiftly pass us by,
You lend your strength to every part,
A vital role in every start.
In buildings tall, you stand so strong,
A pillar of support all along.
Your shimmering surface, sleek and grand,
Reflects the dreams of human hand.
In packaging, you guard with care,
Preserving goods beyond compare.

From cans that hold our favorite drink,
To foil that keeps our food in sync.
 In homes, you shine with elegance,
Adorning windows, a brilliant presence.
With frames that hold our memories dear,
You bring us joy year after year.
 In technology, you play a role,
Conducting currents, a vital soul.
From laptops to smartphones in our hand,
You connect us all, a modern band.
 In progress, you've left your mark,
A material strong, both light and dark.
From bridges spanning wide and far,
To satellites that twinkle like a star.
 But beyond your strength and radiant gleam,
There's more to you than what may seem.
You're sustainable, recyclable too,
Reducing waste, a gift to view.
 Aluminum, oh noble friend,
Your versatility knows no end.
From industry to progress and more,
You're a metal we'll forever adore.

THIRTY-TWO

CONNECTS US ALL

In Aluminum's realm, we find,
A metal of remarkable kind.
With silvery shine and strength untold,
Its story is waiting to unfold.
A champion of sustainability,
Recyclable with great ability.
From cans to cars, it takes its form,
A material that can transform.
In aerospace, it takes to the sky,
With lightweight wings, it learns to fly.
From satellites to space shuttles grand,
Aluminum shapes the unknown land.
In buildings tall, it stands so proud,
A structure strong, amidst the crowd.
From windows gleaming to beams so high,
Aluminum reaches for the sky.

In technology, it plays its part,
Connecting circuits with a spark.
A conductor of electricity,
Aluminum fuels our creativity.

In packaging, it does its share,
Preserving freshness with utmost care.
From cans to foil, it keeps things neat,
Reducing waste, a noble feat.

From bicycles to kitchenware,
Aluminum's touch is everywhere.
With strength and versatility,
It leaves a lasting legacy.

So let us celebrate this metal true,
For all the wonders it can do.
Aluminum, a gift to behold,
A material that connects us all.

THIRTY-THREE

FILLS US WITH GLEE

In packaging, Aluminum shines bright,
A shield, protecting goods day and night.
From cans to foils, its presence is seen,
Preserving freshness, keeping things clean.
  In space exploration, it takes to the sky,
A lightweight metal that helps us fly.
From rockets to satellites, it plays its part,
A sturdy companion, a work of art.
  In sustainability, Aluminum is key,
Recyclable, reusable, setting us free.
Reducing waste, minimizing our strife,
A friend to the Earth, sustaining our life.
  From buildings to cars, it lends its might,
A versatile metal, a true delight.
In industries wide, it finds its place,
A symbol of progress, a mark of grace.

Oh Aluminum, you shine so bright,
A metal of wonder, a guiding light.
In packaging, space, and sustainability,
Your presence, dear Aluminum, fills us with glee.

THIRTY-FOUR

RECYCLABLE, SUSTAINABLE

In a world of metals, bright and strong,
There stands one that sings a different song.
Aluminum, the versatile and true,
A metal that connects me and you.

In kitchens, it plays a vital role,
Preserving freshness, keeping food whole.
From foil to cans, it wraps with care,
Shielding flavors, a culinary affair.

But Aluminum's reach goes far and wide,
In technology, it stands with pride.
With conductivity, it ignites the spark,
Powering devices, lighting up the dark.

In construction, it stands tall and bold,
A pillar of strength, a story untold.

From buildings to bridges, it bears the load,
A testament to its mighty abode.
    And when the heavens call, Aluminum flies,
A companion to stars, up in the skies.
In spacecraft and satellites, it soars,
Exploring the unknown, unlocking new doors.
    But Aluminum's beauty lies not just in might,
It's the way it embraces the world's plight.
Recyclable, sustainable, it takes a stand,
Reducing waste, protecting our land.
    So let us celebrate this metal divine,
Aluminum, a treasure, for all time.
A symbol of progress, connecting us all,
In its shining embrace, we stand tall.

THIRTY-FIVE

BRIGHTER REALITY

In realms of strength, Aluminum stands tall,
A metal versatile, answering the call.
With shining grace, it weaves its lore,
Embracing industries, forevermore.

In skies of planes, Aluminum soars,
As wings of freedom, it proudly adores.
From heights it glides, defying gravity,
A symbol of progress, with tenacity.

From cans to cars, it takes its form,
Aluminum, a substance to transform.
Its lightness and might, a perfect blend,
Innovating, creating, till the end.

In buildings high, it builds the frame,
A structure sturdy, bearing no shame.
With elegance and poise, it stands erect,
Supporting dreams, architects select.

From wires to cables, it connects us all,
Aluminum's touch, a lifeline we recall.
In technology's realm, it finds its place,
Linking hearts, bridging time and space.

With sustainability as its guiding light,
Aluminum shines, in the fight.
Recyclable, it gives the Earth a chance,
To heal and thrive, in its cosmic dance.

So let us hail this mighty metal true,
Aluminum, we owe much to you.
In progress, strength, and sustainability,
You hold the key, for a brighter reality.

ABOUT THE AUTHOR

Walter the Educator is one of the pseudonyms for Walter Anderson. Formally educated in Chemistry, Business, and Education, he is an educator, an author, a diverse entrepreneur, and he is the son of a disabled war veteran. "Walter the Educator" shares his time between educating and creating. He holds interests and owns several creative projects that entertain, enlighten, enhance, and educate, hoping to inspire and motivate you.

Follow, find new works, and stay up to date
with Walter the Educator™
at WaltertheEducator.com

Milton Keynes UK
Ingram Content Group UK Ltd.
UKHW020653201123
432908UK00019B/2312